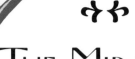

THE MIRACLES OF JESUS

Adapted by
Etta G. Wilson

Illustrations by
Gary Torrisi

Publications International, Ltd.

After Jesus was baptized, he began to travel around, preaching and teaching. He also performed miracles for many people. People began to follow Jesus because they wanted to hear him teach and see the miracles he performed.

But Jesus did not perform the miracles to be seen and admired. He often told the people not to tell what he had done.

Many people knew he had great power and believed Jesus was really the Son of God.

෴

Jesus performed his first miracle at a wedding.

In the middle of the wedding feast, the hosts ran out of wine. They were very upset. But Jesus told the servants to fill six big stone jars with water. Then he told them to give some of it to the man in charge of the feast.

When the man tasted it, the water had turned into wine! He was very surprised. He said to the bridegroom, "This wine is better than the first! You have saved the best wine for last."

Once, in the town of Capernaum, an army officer asked Jesus to heal his servant, who was very sick. The officer was worried because he cared about his servant very much.

Jesus said that he would come to the officer's house. But the officer said, "Lord, I am not worthy to have you enter my house. I know you can heal my servant from here."

Jesus was happy to meet a man with so much faith. Without taking another step, he healed the servant. It was a miracle!

Soon, many people heard about Jesus' miracles and wanted to see him. Great crowds began to follow Jesus wherever he went.

In one large crowd, there was a woman who had been sick for twelve years. She had gone to see many doctors but she only got worse.

The woman had heard about Jesus, so she came up behind him in the crowd. She said to herself, "If only I can touch his clothes, I will be well."

She reached out and touched Jesus' robe. At that very moment, she was healed!

Jesus stopped and turned around. "Who touched my clothes?" he said.

The woman came forward and knelt down in front of Jesus. She was shaking with fear, but she told Jesus the whole story.

Jesus said to her, "You are now well because you believed in me. You won't have any more pain. Go in peace."

Once, Jesus was walking in the city of Jericho. A blind man by the name of Bartimaeus was there. When he heard Jesus coming, he shouted, "Jesus, have mercy on me!"

When Jesus asked what he wanted, Bartimaeus said, "Teacher, I want to see again."

"Go on your way," Jesus told him. "Your eyes are healed because of your faith."

Bartimaeus could see at once. He went away happy and praising God.

Another time, Jesus spent a whole day teaching a crowd of nearly five thousand people about the Kingdom of God.

As the sun went down, the disciples told Jesus that he should send the people away to look for food and shelter.

"You give them something to eat," Jesus answered.

The disciples were surprised because they only had five loaves of bread and two fish.

"Tell everyone to sit down," said Jesus.

When everyone was seated on the ground, Jesus took the five loaves and the two fish. He looked up to heaven and blessed the food. Then he broke it into pieces and told the disciples to pass out the food.

What a supper they had! Everyone ate until they were full. Afterward, the disciples collected twelve baskets of leftovers. How could so many people eat from so little? It was a miracle!

Soon after this, Jesus' disciples were crossing the Sea of Galilee in a boat. Suddenly, they saw Jesus walking on the water toward them!

Peter told Jesus that he wanted to walk on the water, too. So Jesus told Peter to come to him. Peter got out and started walking on the water. But he became afraid and started sinking. Jesus reached out and saved Peter.

In the boat, the disciples knelt down before Jesus and said, "Truly, you are God's Son."